THE BEATLES
easy playalong *for* recorder

WISE PUBLICATIONS
London/New York/Paris/Sydney/Copenhagen/Madrid/Tokyo

Exclusive Distributors:
Music Sales Limited
8/9 Frith Street,
London W1V 5TZ, England.

Music Sales Pty Limited
120 Rothschild Avenue,
Rosebery, NSW 2018,
Australia.

Order No. NO90693
ISBN 0-7119-7809-3
This book © Copyright 2000 by Wise Publications.

Music compiled and arranged by Paul Honey.
Music processed by Enigma Music Production Services.
Cover photography courtesy George Taylor.
Printed in the United Kingdom by
Printwise (Haverhill) Ltd., Suffolk.

CD produced by Paul Honey.
Instrumental solos by Andy Finden.
All guitars by Arthur Dick.
Engineered by Kester Sims.

Your Guarantee of Quality:
As publishers, we strive to produce every book to
the highest commercial standards.
The music has been freshly engraved and the book
has been carefully designed to minimise awkward page
turns and to make playing from it a real pleasure.
Particular care has been given to specifying acid-free,
neutral-sized paper made from pulps which have not
been elemental chlorine bleached.
This pulp is from farmed sustainable forests and
was produced with special regard for the environment.
Throughout, the printing and binding have been planned
to ensure a sturdy, attractive publication which should
give years of enjoyment.
If your copy fails to meet our high standards,
please inform us and we will gladly replace it.

Music Sales' complete catalogue describes
thousands of titles and is available in full colour
sections by subject, direct from Music Sales Limited.
Please state your areas of interest and send
a cheque/postal order for £1.50 for postage to:
Music Sales Limited, Newmarket Road,
Bury St. Edmunds, Suffolk IP33 3YB.

www.musicsales.com

Junior Guest Spot

Eleanor Rigby 6

The Fool On The Hill 7

Hey Jude 8

Lady Madonna 10

Let It Be 12

Michelle 14

Norwegian Wood 16

Ob-La-Di, Ob-La-Da 18

Penny Lane 20

She Loves You 22

She's Leaving Home 32

When I'm Sixty Four 24

While My Guitar Gently Weeps 26

Yellow Submarine 28

Yesterday 30

Recorder Fingering Chart 4

RECORDER FINGERING CHART

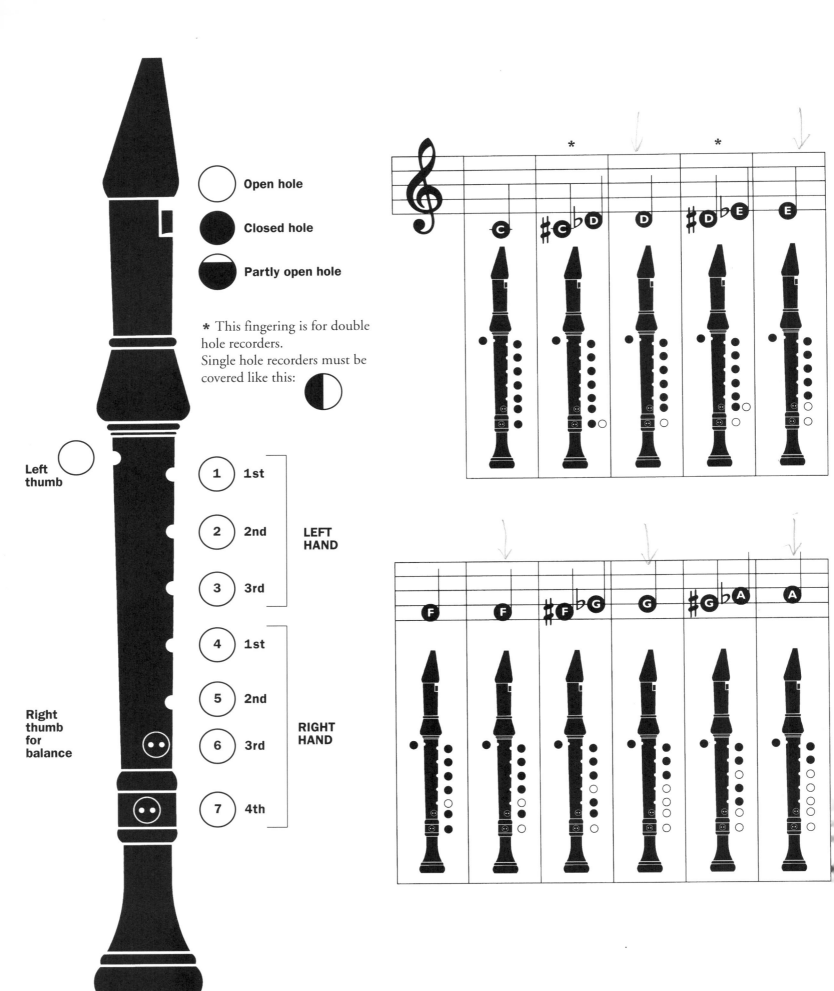

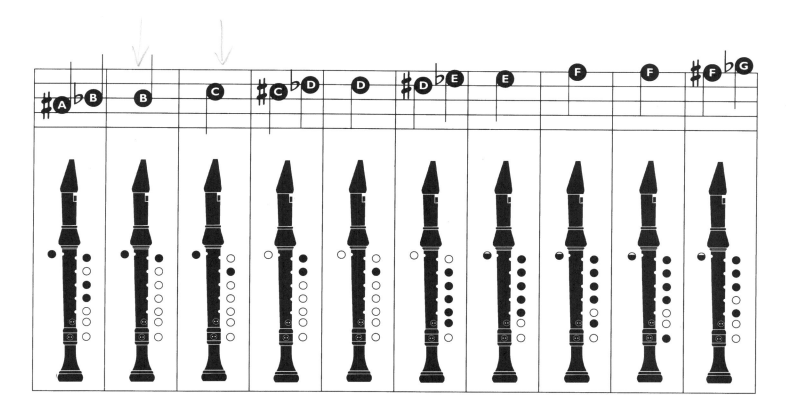

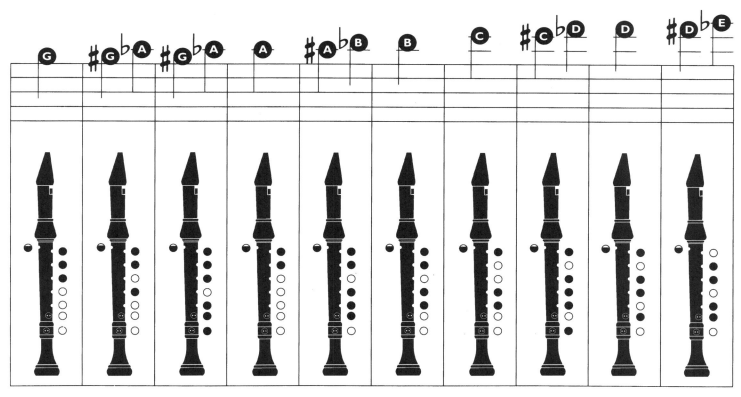

ELEANOR RIGBY

Words & Music by John Lennon & Paul McCartney

THE FOOL ON THE HILL

Words & Music by John Lennon & Paul McCartney

HEY JUDE

Words & Music by John Lennon & Paul McCartney

Hey Jude don't make it bad, take a

sad song — and make it bet - ter. — Re - mem - ber to let her in - to your

heart, then you can start — to make it bet - ter.

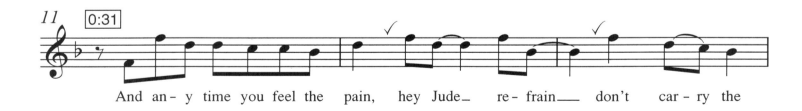

And an - y time you feel the pain, hey Jude — re - frain — don't car - ry the

world up - on — your shoul - ders. For well you know that it's a

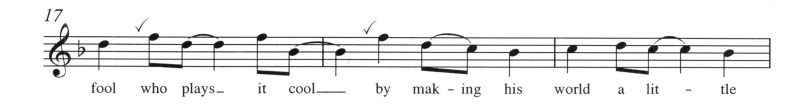
fool who plays_ it cool_ by mak- ing his world a lit - tle

cold - er. Da da da da_ da da da da da. Hey_

Jude don't make it bad, take a sad song_ and make it bet ter._ Re -

-mem-ber to let her un-der your skin, then you be - gin_ to make it bet- -

- ter. Da da da da da da da da da da Hey_ Jude

Da da da da da da da da da da Hey_ Jude.

LADY MADONNA

Words & Music by John Lennon & Paul McCartney

Mon - day's child has learned to tie his boot - lace,_____
Thurs - day night your stock - ings need - ed mend - ing._____

See how they run._____

La - dy Ma - don - na, ba - by at your breast;

won - der how you man - age to feed_____ the rest._____

La - dy Ma - don - na, child - ren at your feet;

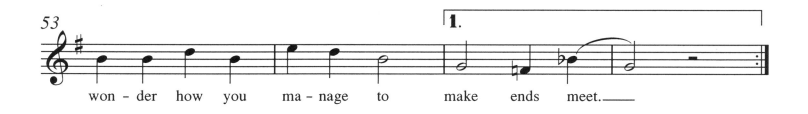

won - der how you ma - nage to make ends meet._____

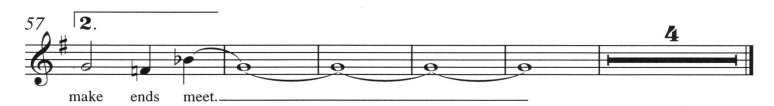

make ends meet._____

LET IT BE

Words & Music by John Lennon & Paul McCartney

Shine un - til to - mor - row, Let it be.⎯ I

wake up to the sound of mu - sic, Moth-er Ma ⎯ ry comes to me,

speak - ing words of wis - dom, Let it be.⎯ Let it

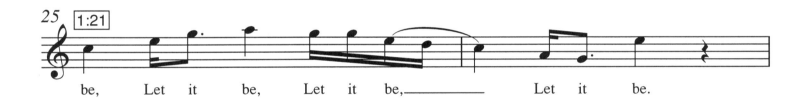

be, Let it be, Let it be,⎯⎯ Let it be.

There will be an an - swer, Let it be.⎯ Let it

be, Let it be, Let it be,⎯⎯ Let it be.

There will be an ans - wer, Let it be.⎯⎯

MICHELLE

Words & Music by John Lennon & Paul McCartney

Gently

Mi - chelle, ma belle, these are words that

go to - geth - er well, my Mi - chelle. Mi - chelle, ma belle,

sont les mots qui vont très bien en - semble, très bien en - semble. I

love you, I love you, I love you. That's all I want to

say. Un - til I find a way_____ I will

say the on - ly words I know that you'll un - der - stand.

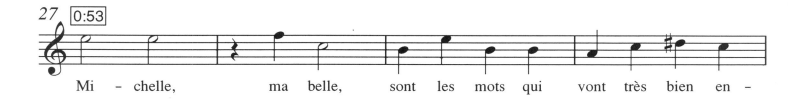

27 [0:53]
Mi – chelle, ma belle, sont les mots qui vont très bien en –

31
– semble, très bien en – semble. I need to, I need to, I need to,

35
I need to make you see oh what you mean to me.___ Un –

39
– til I do, I'm hop – ing you will know what I mean.

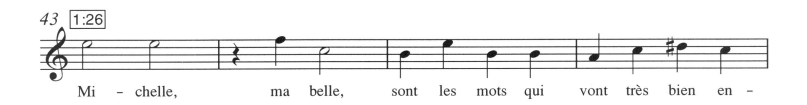

43 [1:26]
Mi – chelle, ma belle, sont les mots qui vont très bien en –

47
– semble, très bien en – semble. I will say the on – ly

50
words I know that you'll un – der – stand, my Mi – chelle.

NORWEGIAN WOOD

Words & Music by John Lennon & Paul McCartney

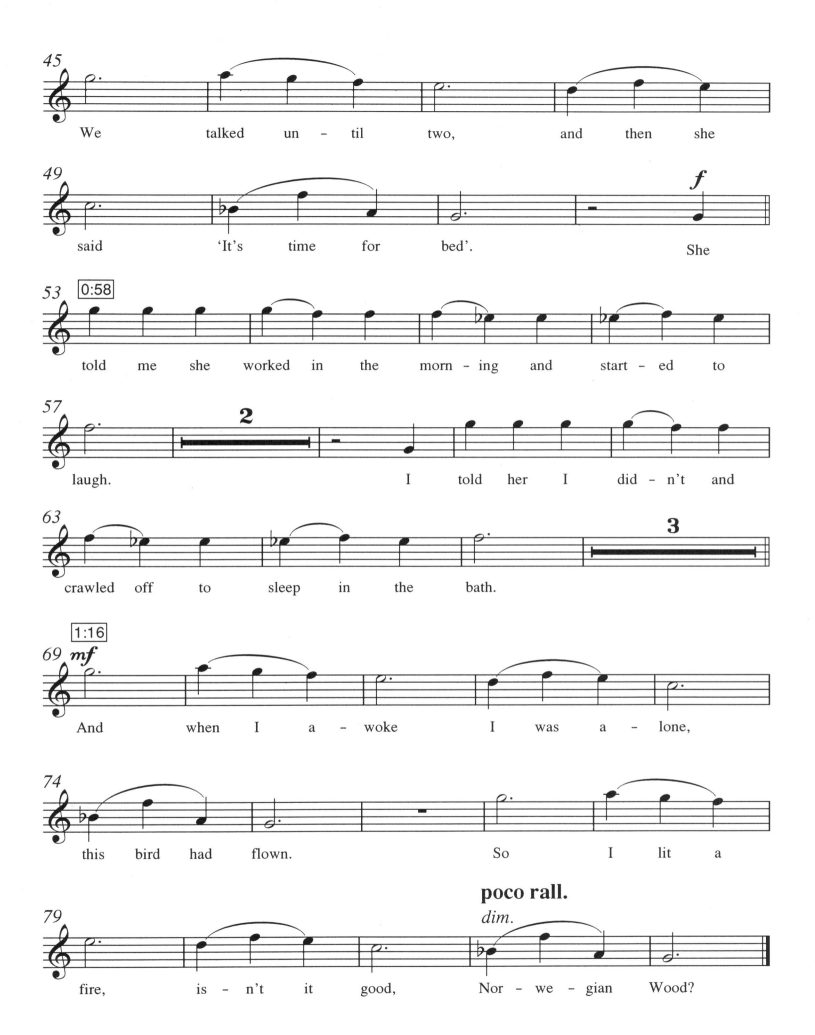

OB-LA-DI, OB-LA-DA

Words & Music by John Lennon & Paul McCartney

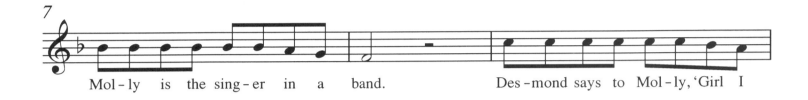

La la how the life goes on.

0:44

Des-mond takes a trol-ley to the jewel-ler's store, buys a twen-ty car-at gold-en

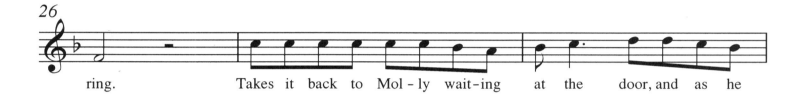

ring. Takes it back to Mol-ly wait-ing at the door, and as he

1:00

gives it to her she be-gins to sing. Ob-la-di,—— Ob-la-da,— life goes on—

— bra, la la how the life goes on. Ob-la-di,——

— ob-la-da,— life goes on—— bra, La la how the life goes on.

PENNY LANE

Words & Music by John Lennon & Paul McCartney

Moderately

Pen - ny Lane, there is a bar - ber show - ing

pho - to - graphs of ev - 'ry head he's had the plea - sure to_____ know. And all the

peo - ple that come and go stop and say 'hel - lo.' On the

cor - ner is a bank - er with a mo - tor car, the lit - tle child - ren laugh at him be - hind his

back. And the ban - ker nev - er wears a mac in the pour - ing rain.

Ve - ry strange! Pen - ny Lane is in my ears and in my eyes,

there be - neath the blue su - bur - ban skies I sit, and mean - while back in Pen - ny

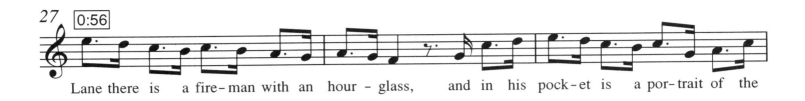

Lane there is a fire-man with an hour-glass, and in his pock-et is a por-trait of the

Queen. He likes to keep his fire-en-gine clean, it's a clean ma-chine.

Pen-ny Lane, the bar-ber shaves an-oth-er cus-to-mer, we see the

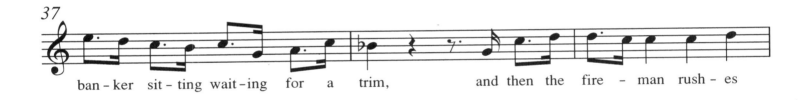

ban-ker sit-ting wait-ing for a trim, and then the fire-man rush-es

in, from the pour-ing rain. Ve-ry strange! Pen-ny

Lane is in my ears and in my eyes,

there be-neath the blue su-bur-ban skies.

SHE LOVES YOU

Words & Music by John Lennon & Paul McCartney

al -most lost her mind.____ And now she says she knows you're

not the hurt - ing kind,____ she says she loves you and you know that can't be

bad. yes she loves you, and you know you should be glad.

She loves you, yeah yeah yeah. She loves you yeah

yeah yeah, and with a love like that, you know you should be glad.____

With a love like that, you know you should be glad._____

With a love like that, you know you should be glad._____

WHEN I'M SIXTY FOUR

Words & Music by John Lennon & Paul McCartney

When I get old-er, los-ing my hair

ma-ny years from now. Will you still be send-ing me a val-en-tine,

birth-day greet-ings, bot-tle of wine?__ If I'd been out 'til quar-ter to three

would you lock the door? Will you still need me, will you still feed me,

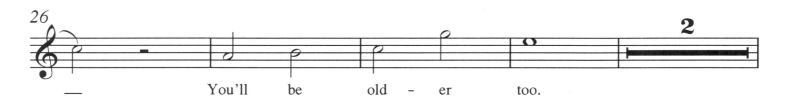

when I'm six-ty four? Oo.__

You'll be old-er too.

And if you say the word_____ I could

stay with you. **2** 1:09 Send me a post - card,

drop me a line, stat- ing point of view. In - di - cate pre - cise - ly what you

mean to say, yours sin- cere - ly wast- ing a - way.__ Give me your ans - wer,

fill in a form, mine for - ev - er more. Will you still need me,

will you still feed me, when I'm six - ty four? **4**

WHILE MY GUITAR GENTLY WEEPS

Words & Music by George Harrison

Rather slow

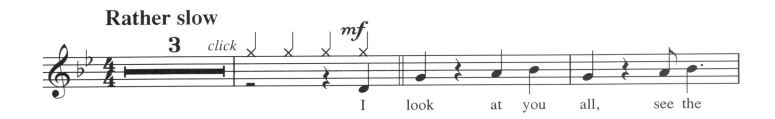

I look at you all, see the

love there that's sleep - ing, while my gui -

- tar gent - ly weeps. I look at the

floor and I see it needs sweep - ing,

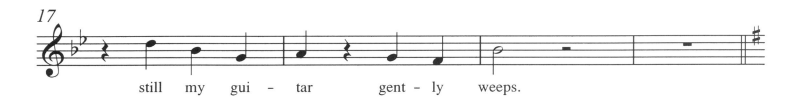

still my gui - tar gent - ly weeps.

I don't know why_____ no-bo-dy told____ you

how to un - fold your love. I don't know

how_____ some -one con - trolled you, they bought and

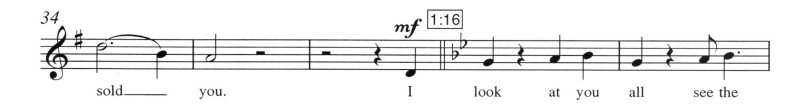

mf 1:16

sold_____ you. I look at you all see the

love there that's sleep - ing, while my gui - tar gent - ly

weeps. With ev - 'ry mis - take we must sure - ly be

learn - ing. Still my gui - tar gent - ly weeps.

YELLOW SUBMARINE

Words & Music by John Lennon & Paul McCartney

Moderately

In the town___ where I was born   lived a

man___   who sailed to sea.   And he told___ us of his

life   in the land___   of sub - ma - rines.   So we

sailed___   on to the sun   'til we found___   the sea of

green.   And we lived___   be - neath the waves   in our

yel - low sub - ma - rine.   We all live in a yel-low sub - ma - rine,

yel - low sub - ma - rine,   yel - low sub - ma - rine.   We all live in a

yel - low sub - ma - rine,   yel - low sub - ma - rine,   yel - low sub - ma - rine. And our

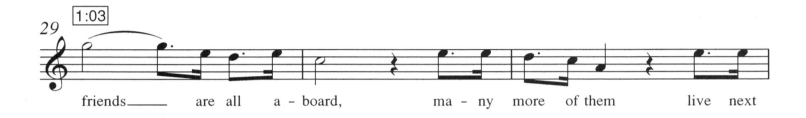

friends_____ are all a - board,   ma - ny more of them live next

door.   And the band_____ be - gins to play:

We all live in a yel - low sub - ma - rine,   yel - low sub - ma - rine,

yel - low sub - ma - rine.   We all live in a yel - low sub - ma - rine,

yel - low sub - ma - rine,   yel - low sub - ma - rine.   yel - low sub - ma - rine.

YESTERDAY

Words & Music by John Lennon & Paul McCartney

Yes-ter-day, all my trou-bles seemed so

far a-way, now it looks as though they're here to stay,— oh

I be-lieve in yes-ter-day.— Sud-den-ly

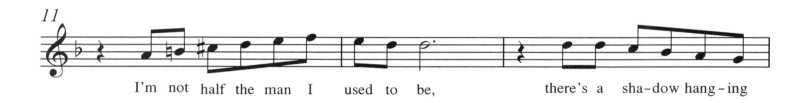

I'm not half the man I used to be, there's a sha-dow hang-ing

o-ver me,— oh yes-ter-day came sud-den-ly.—

Why she had to go I don't know, she would-n't say.

I said some-thing wrong, now I long for yes - ter - day.

1:09
mp

Yes - ter - day love was such an ea - sy game to play,

now I need a place to hide a - way,— oh I be - lieve in

1:30

yes - ter - day.— Yes - ter - day love was such an ea - sy

game to play, now I need a place to hide a - way,— oh

slower

I be - lieve in yes - ter - day.— *dim.*

SHE'S LEAVING HOME

Words & Music by John Lennon & Paul McCartney

Flowing